KinderClips

EARLY LEARNING PATTERNS

by Marilynn G. Barr

Publisher: Roberta Suid
Editor: Carol Whiteley

ISBN 1-878279-19-X
Printed in the United States of America
9 8 7 6 5 4 3 2

For a complete catalog,
write to the address above.

Table of Contents

INTRODUCTION

KinderClips includes a wide variety of patterns you can use in your classroom throughout the year. Turn them into flashcards, puppets, folder and chart decorations, game pieces, concept reinforcers, greeting cards—there are so many ways to use these creative materials.

How to Use These Patterns

Alphabet Patterns
Every letter of the alphabet, both upper- and lower-case, is included here, with a picture for each letter to boot. Children can make miniature alphabet booklets by stapling the letters and matching pictures together in sequence. Or each week you can supply the children with an upper- and lower-case letter and alphabet picture to glue to a sheet of construction paper, along with cutout magazine pictures, to create keepsake alphabet books. Let the children design, color, and decorate covers using both craft materials and clips collection art. The alphabet cards are also perfect for playing Concentration, matching upper- and lower-case letters.

Number Patterns
Learning numbers is fun with the special number character patterns. For counting and simple math practice, let each child choose a set, cut the set apart, and use the pieces as counters during group or individual practice. You can duplicate the numbers (as well as shape, color, and community worker patterns) for a game of Concentration.

Shape Patterns
Children will have fun matching the shape pictures and playing with the giant shape dominos set. Duplicate the shape picture cards and a second set of outline shape cards for a matching activity. To play Dominos, provide each child with a shape domino set. Allow each child to match a domino to one previously played as a reward for good work or good behavior or as a special bonus. To vary a game, fill the shapes with different patterns, magazine pictures, numbers, colored dots, alphabet letters, or art from the card sets or clip collections before you reproduce them. Make sure you have at least two sets of each decoration for matching.

Color
Have children color each picture with a different color. Then provide the color word cards for color word recognition. The color card sets can be used as flashcards, book labels, or gift tags.

Size Patterns
These ready-to-color-and-cut-out patterns are just right for size recognition practice.

Time Concept Patterns
Learning the days of the week, months of the year, and the time of day is easy with the patterns in this section. Patterns of children in morning, afternoon, and night attire create a visual understanding of the passing of time. Turn the patterns into puppets by pasting each side of a puppet to a tongue depressor.

Spatial Concept Patterns
A duck, a bear, a car, a house, and a giraffe teach the children about left and right, up and down, and other spatial concepts. A playroom with miniature toys to place on shelves, in a box, or on a table plus directions, reinforce spatial concepts. The patterns can be cut out and placed in different positions on the playroom pages.

Food Patterns
Have children color these cards, then provide them with paper plates to make a meal to remember. They can also create take-home food group booklets by coloring the patterns, then cutting them out and pasting them to construction paper. The appliance and utensil patterns enhance food study.

Anatomy Patterns
Children can play Simple Simon with these patterns at their desks. Provide each child with either the two-page body parts chart or the head chart, and give them some colored sticker dots. Then let children play the traditional Simple Simon game but with one exception: Instead of touching a body part they place a sticker dot on the part on the chart. A quick glance at their charts will determine who continues playing.

Transportation Patterns
Use these patterns to make your entire classroom a traffic safety school. Reproduce the traffic signal and enlarge the traffic signs to hang from the ceiling or mount on walls, bulletin boards, and desks. Also label desks with familiar neighborhood street signs and buildings. Make headband strips for children and provide each with a vehicle from the transportation clips collection to attach to their headbands. Then choose traffic signal attendants and let traffic school begin, with each child representing a moving vehicle.

Community Worker Patterns
Have children color, cut apart, and match community helpers to their respective vehicles and tools. You can also enlarge these patterns to further develop the transportation section's traffic safety school by letting several children wear police officer headbands and badges.

Plant Patterns
Reinforce plant study with the parts of the plant poster and the Trees, Leaves, and Blooms card set. Use the Potted Plant Poster for a cut-and-paste activity. Take the children on a nature walk to collect leaves for their plant posters. Provide craft supplies to decorate the potted plant.

Animal, Insect, and Pet Patterns

Children are fascinated by all sorts of animals. Here is a wonderful reference library of illustrations for children to use in creating circus and zoo pictures as well as take-home animal scrapbooks.

Weather Patterns

Weather Bee's weather chart tells the class what the weather is like outside. Create a flannel board landscape on which the children can place the weather symbols. Then provide each child with a 3" x 12" oaktag or construction paper strip and weather symbol cards to color and paste on for a weekly weather report. At the end of the week, choose several children to give an end-of-the-week weather report.

Self-Awareness

Families and family relationships are another fascinating subject for children. The students can make a family tree using the various family picture cards. Provide each child with a large sheet of construction paper and enough 3" x 4" black construction paper frames to glue their pictures to. Have children color the appropriate family pictures and glue them to the black frames. Then have them glue the framed pictures to the construction paper for a keepsake gift. The Make a Happy Face wheel and the paper plate faces will help teach children about emotions.

Clips Collection Patterns

Here is a great resource of clothing, health, classroom symbols, and birthday illustrations you can duplicate or enlarge for classroom displays, decorative art on worksheets, folders, and scrapbooks, and to turn into gifts such as construction paper greeting cards.

Creative Writing Paper

Seasonal art decorates the borders of these lined manuscript papers for letter practice, notes to parents, letters to pen pals, and so on.

School Rules Patterns

Enlarge these mini school rules labels to post on the wall, door, bulletin board, or student desks.

Public Sign Patterns

The patterns in this section will familiarize children with the many public signs and symbols that give directions and information.

Award Patterns

Enthusiastic children will enjoy receiving these classroom or take-home signs of achievement.

Award Badge Patterns

Achievement recognition is one of the best motivators for small children. Reward students with these mini badge awards for a variety of successes.

Craft and Gift Ideas

This section provides you with directions and diagrams for four different projects:

Greeting Cards

The children can decorate these with Clips Collection art.

Refrigerator Magnets

Using food card sets and magnetic tape, children can either mount the patterns on construction paper squares or laminate them and mount the magnetic tape directly on the back. (For durability, have children mount the magnetic tape prior to laminating.)

Family Trees

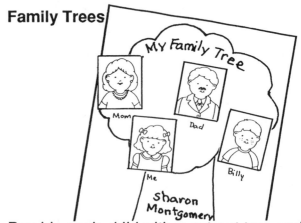

Provide each child with a cut-out tree and a sheet of colored construction paper. Have children color and cut out family pictures to glue on their trees. Help children write their families' names under each picture and then add *My Family Tree* at the top.

Reminder Magnets

Let students decorate these with the health Clips Collection. Add appropriate wording for dental appointments, doctor's appointments, etc.

Alphabet

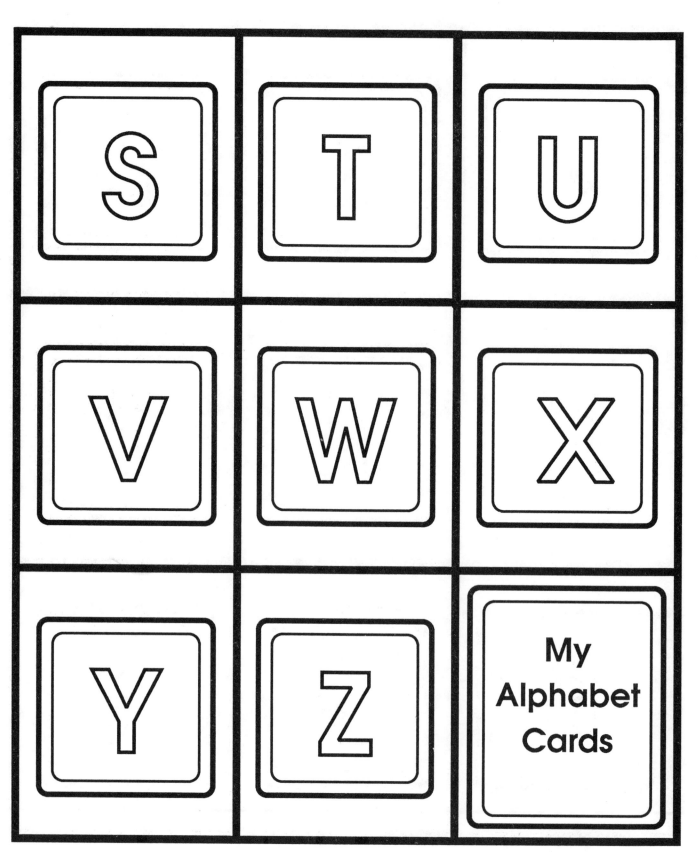

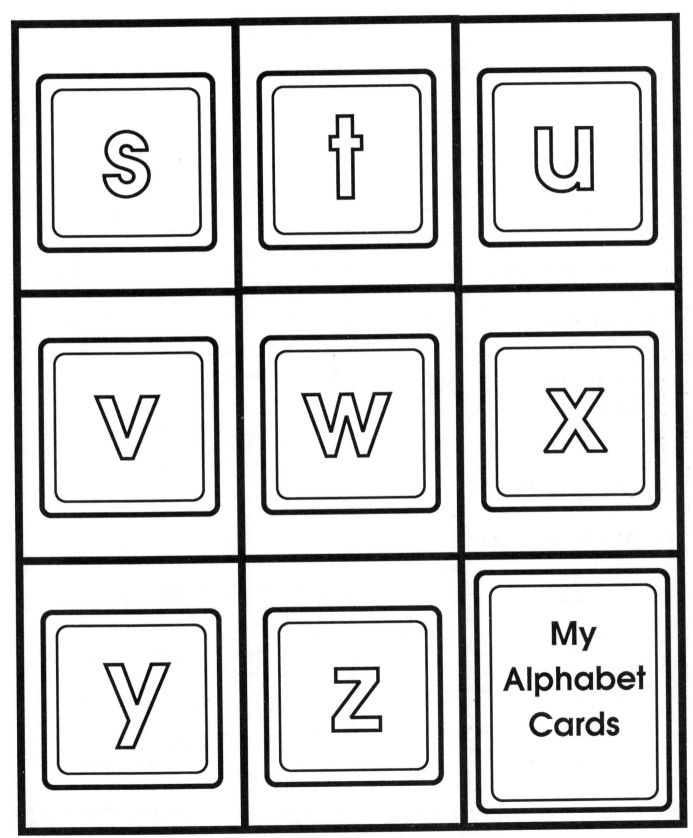

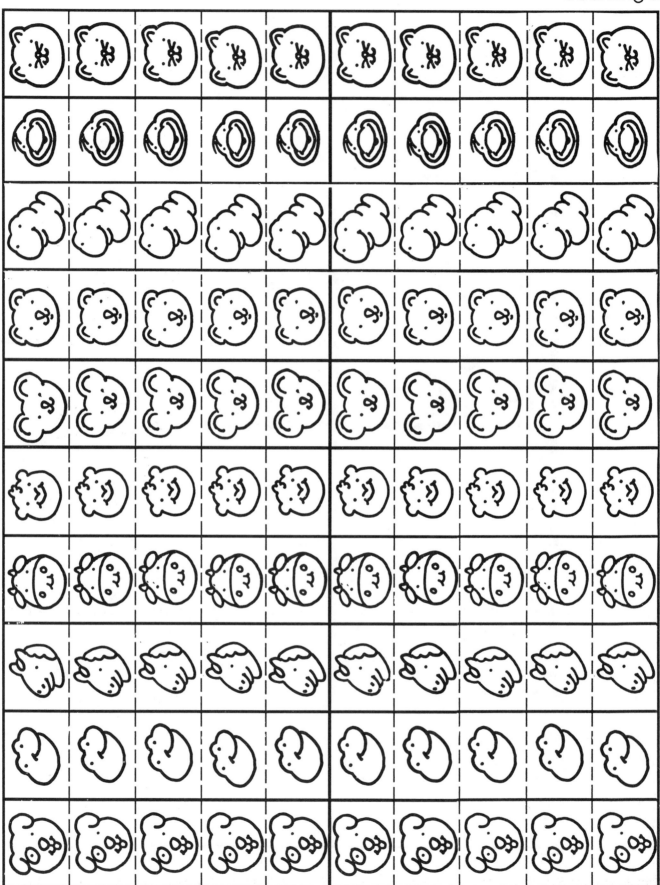

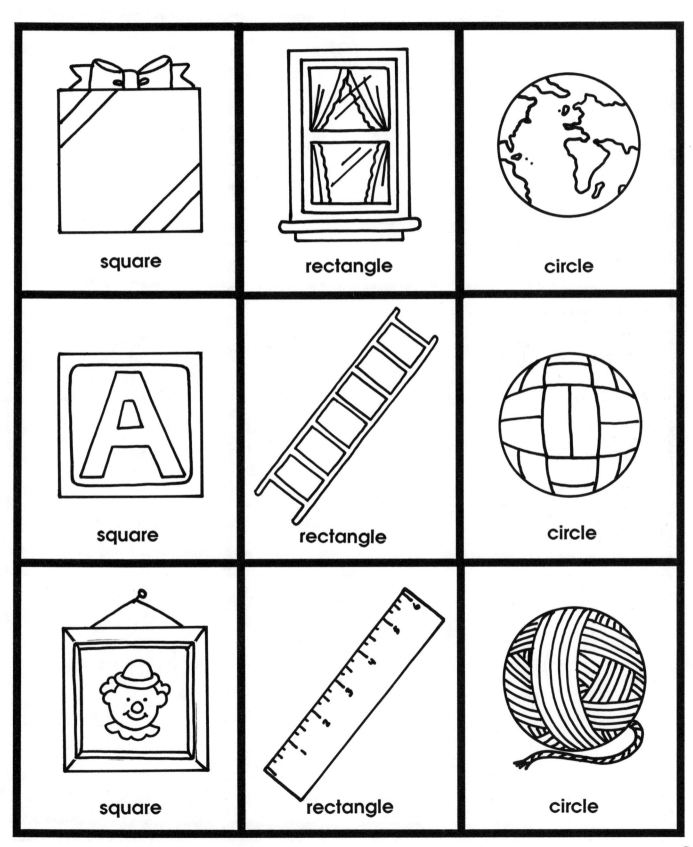

square

rectangle

circle

square

rectangle

circle

square

rectangle

circle

Shapes
Shape Pictures

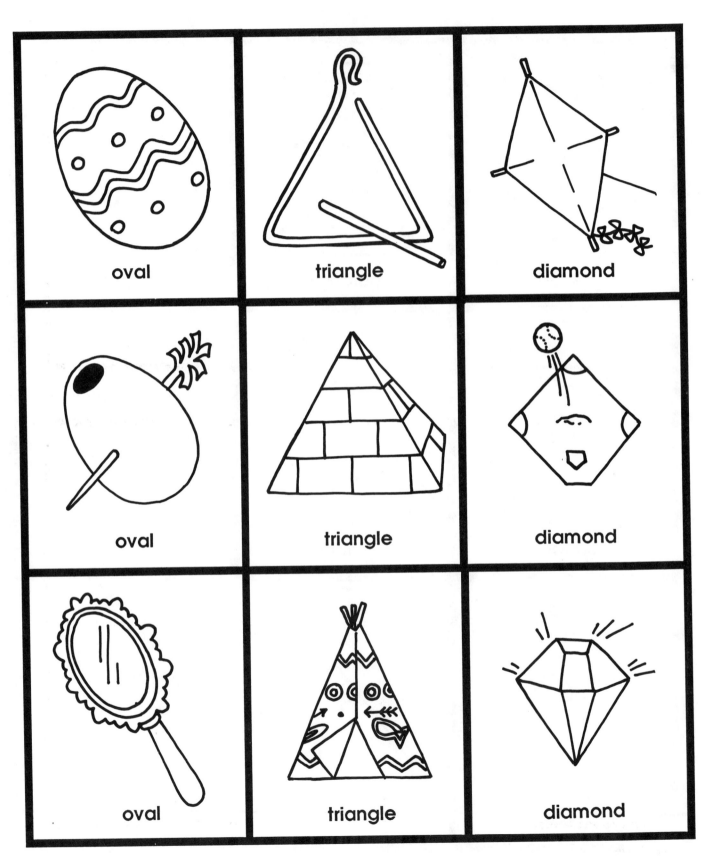

oval

triangle

diamond

oval

triangle

diamond

oval

triangle

diamond

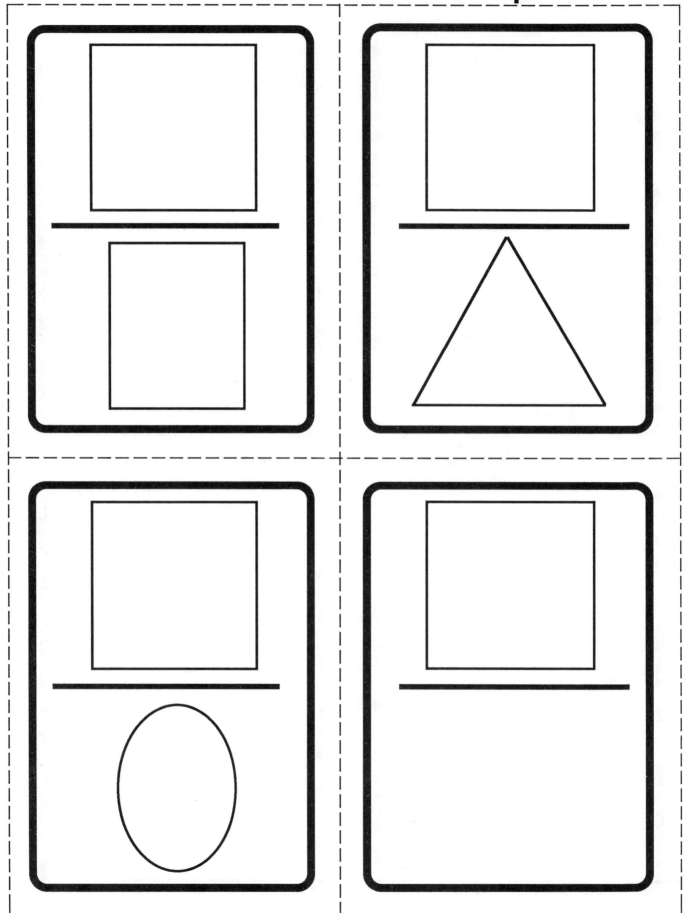

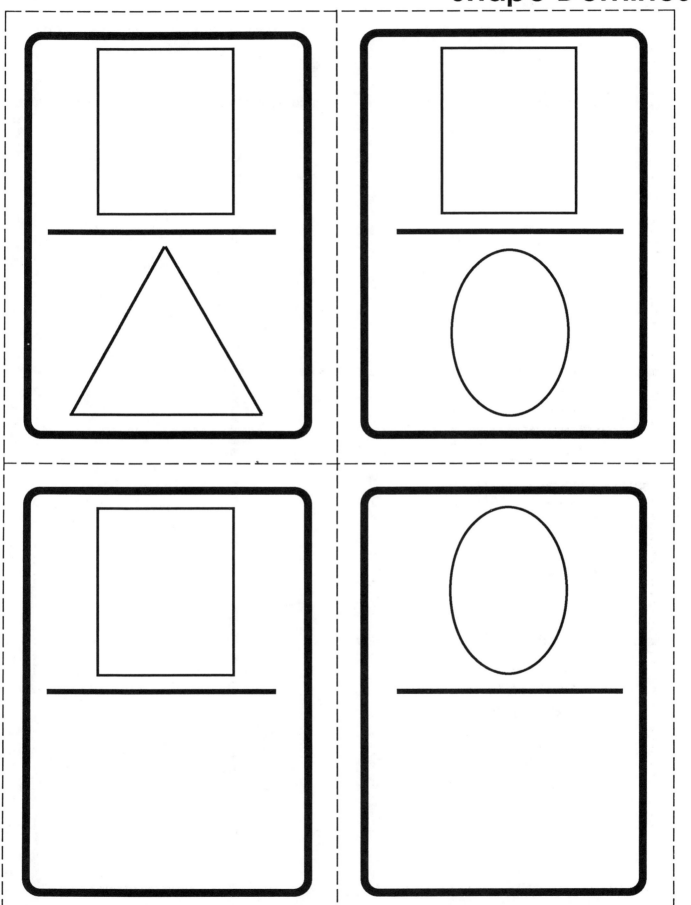

blue	purple	pink
yellow	orange	black
red	green	brown

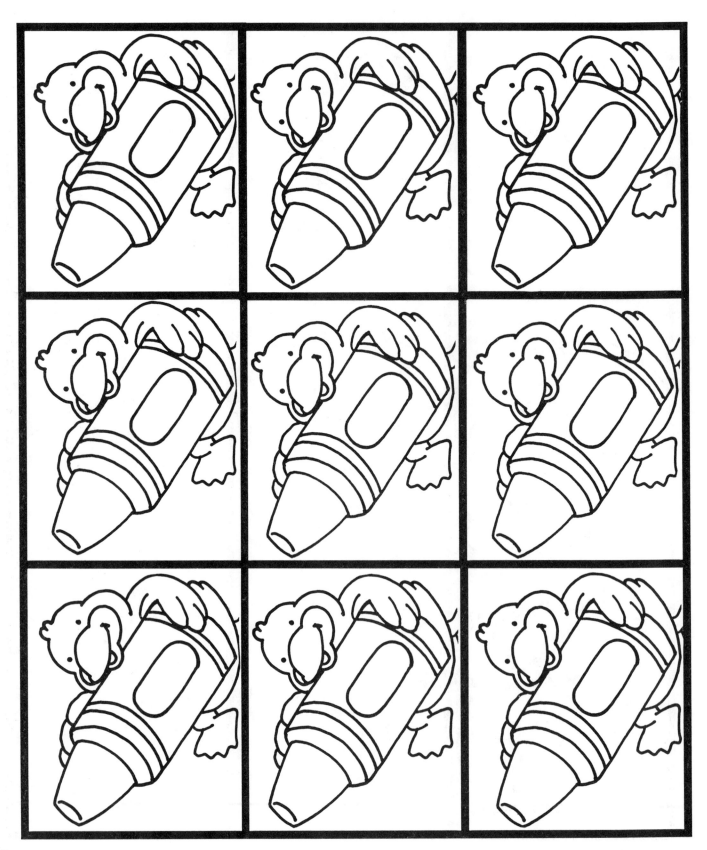

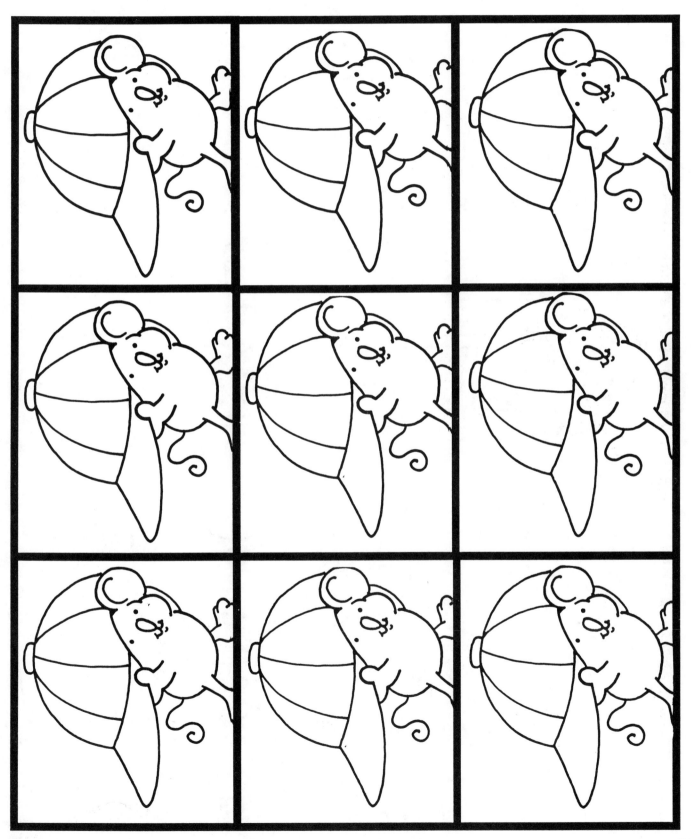

morning

afternoon

day

night

yesterday

tomorrow

Tuesday	Friday	Sunday
Monday	Thursday	Saturday
	Wednesday	

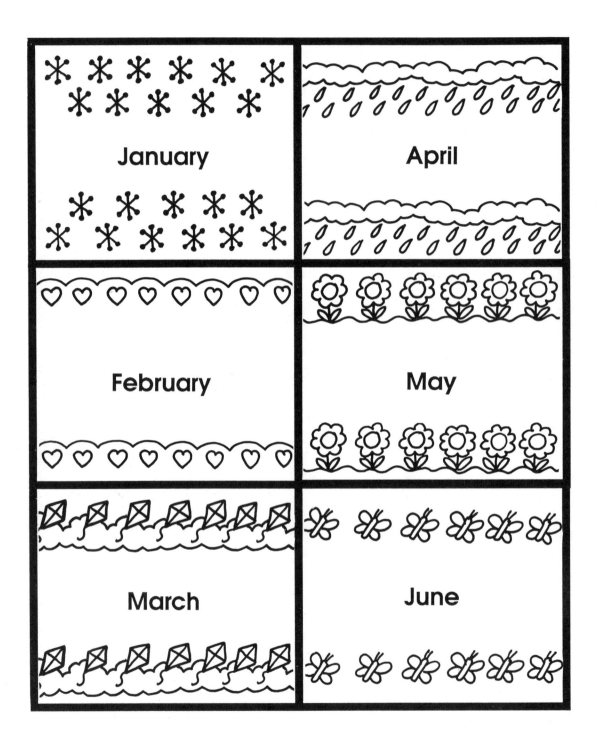

July	October
August	November
September	December

At Home

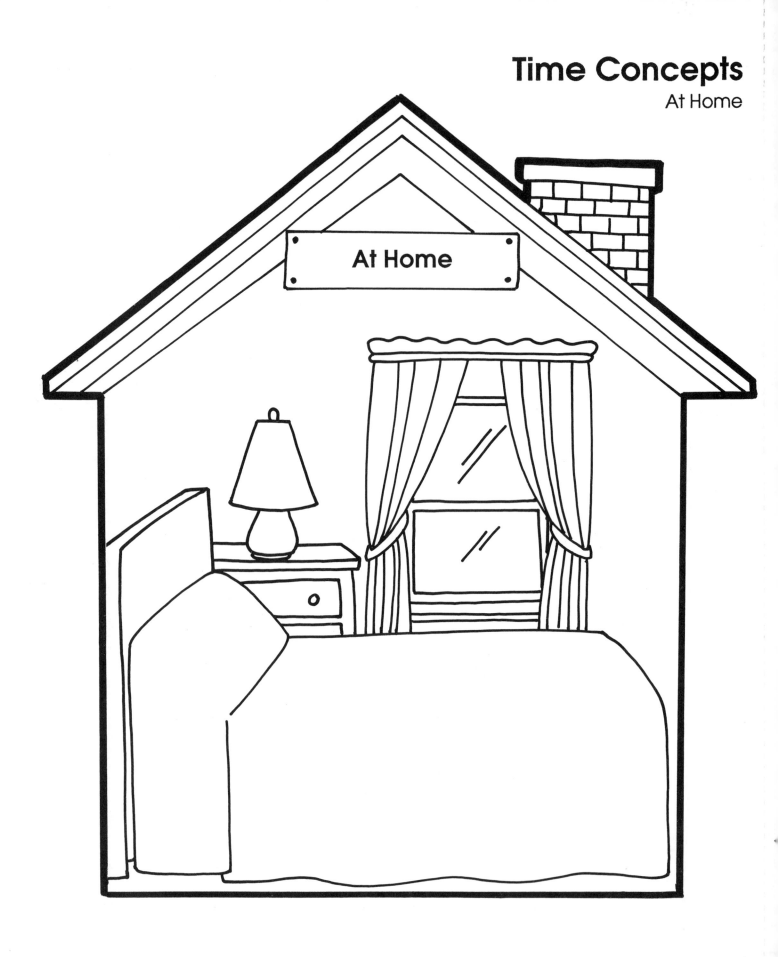

At Home

At Home

At School

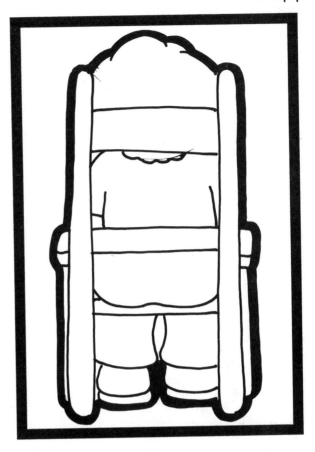

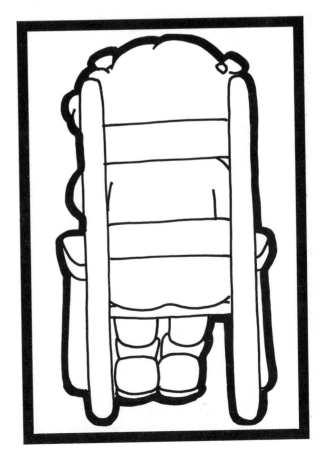

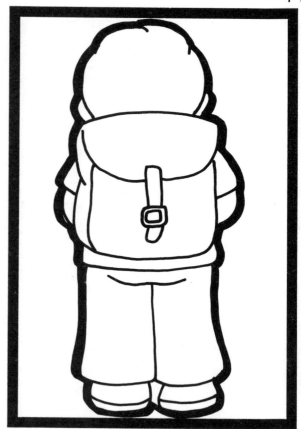

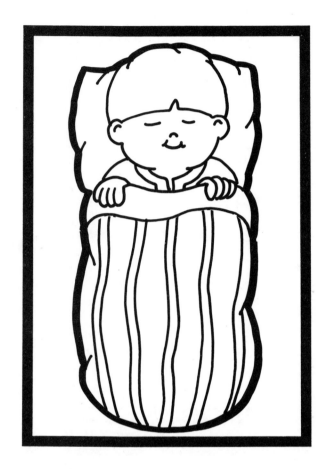

open

closed

outside

inside

over

under

behind

next to

top

bottom

up

down

left

right

front

back

TOY BOX

top

bottom

front   back

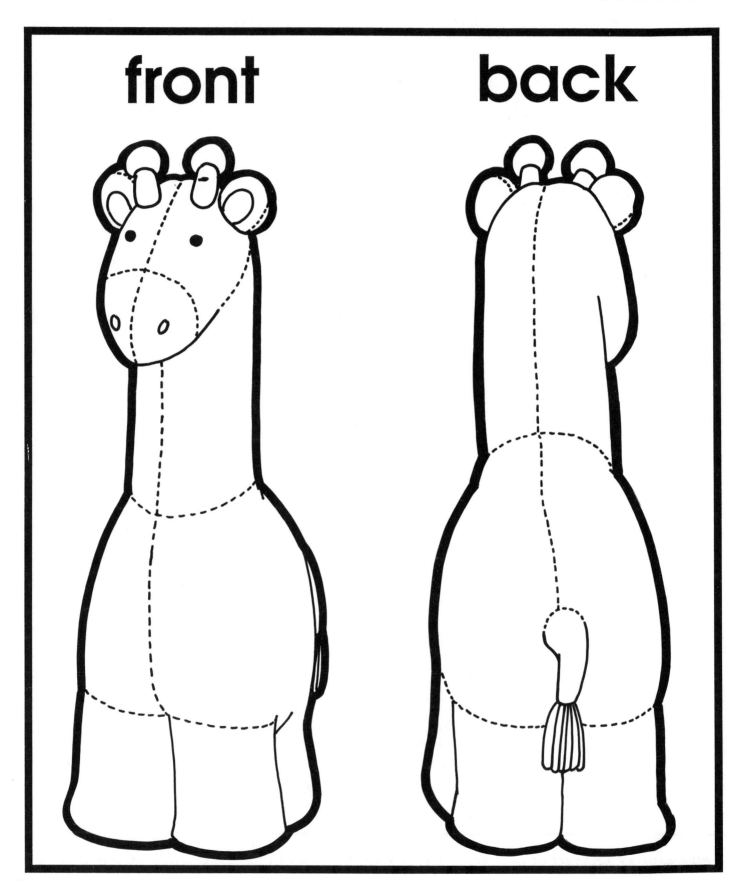

left

right

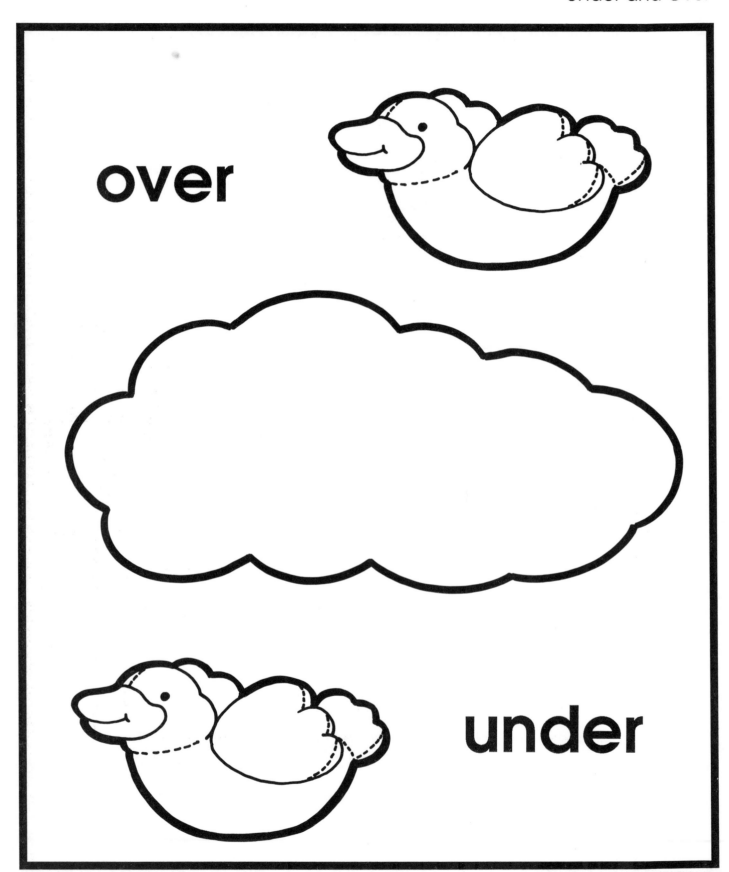

over

under

next to

behind

inside

outside

out

in

HONEY POT

up

down

63

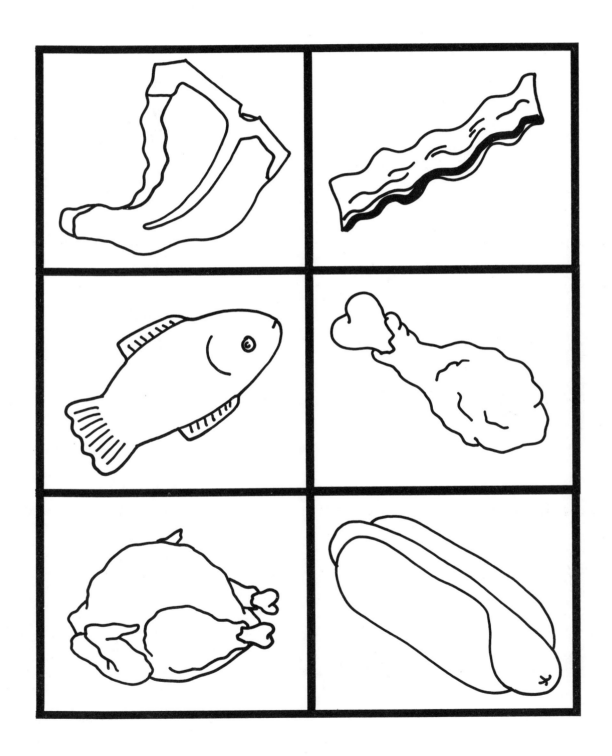

Food
Breads and Grains

66

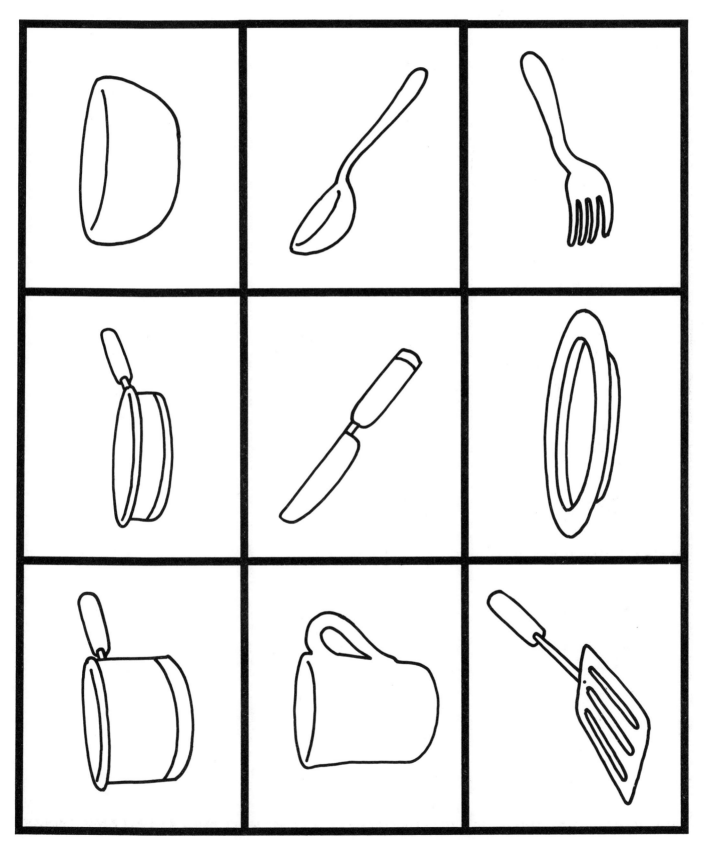

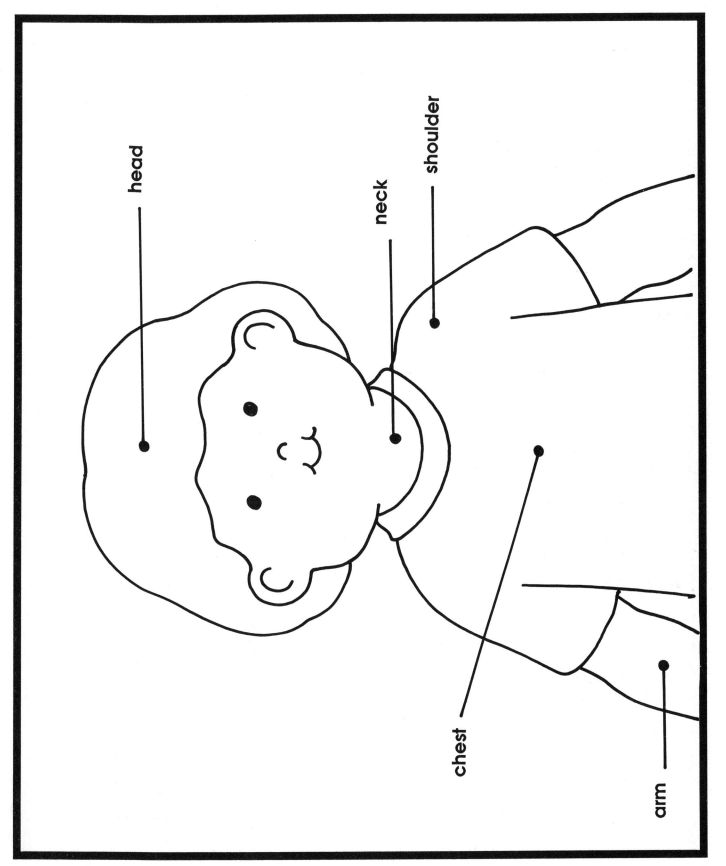

head

neck

shoulder

chest

arm

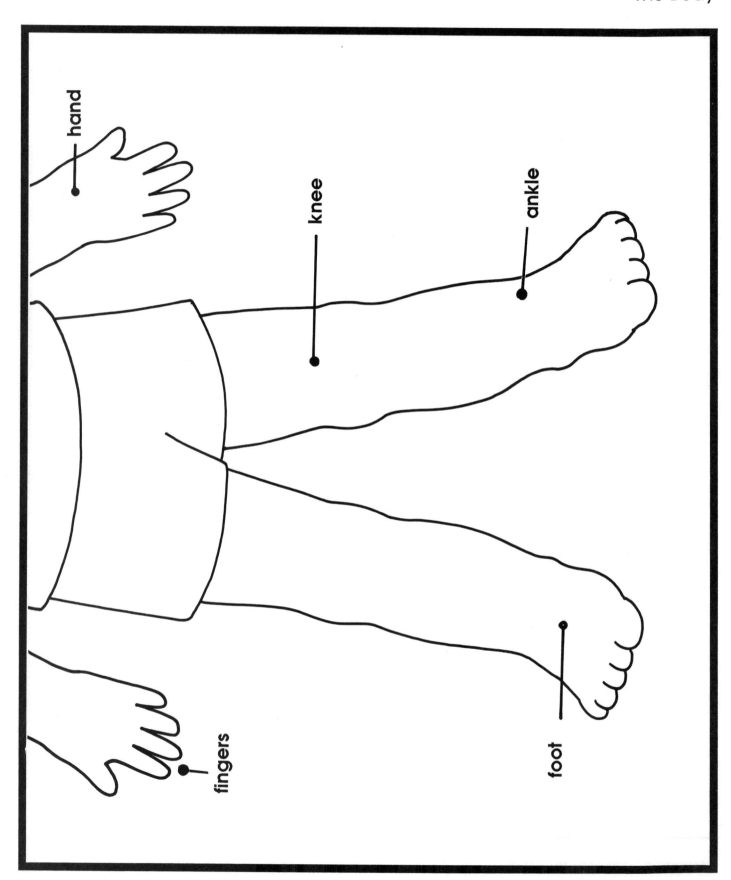

hand

knee

ankle

fingers

foot

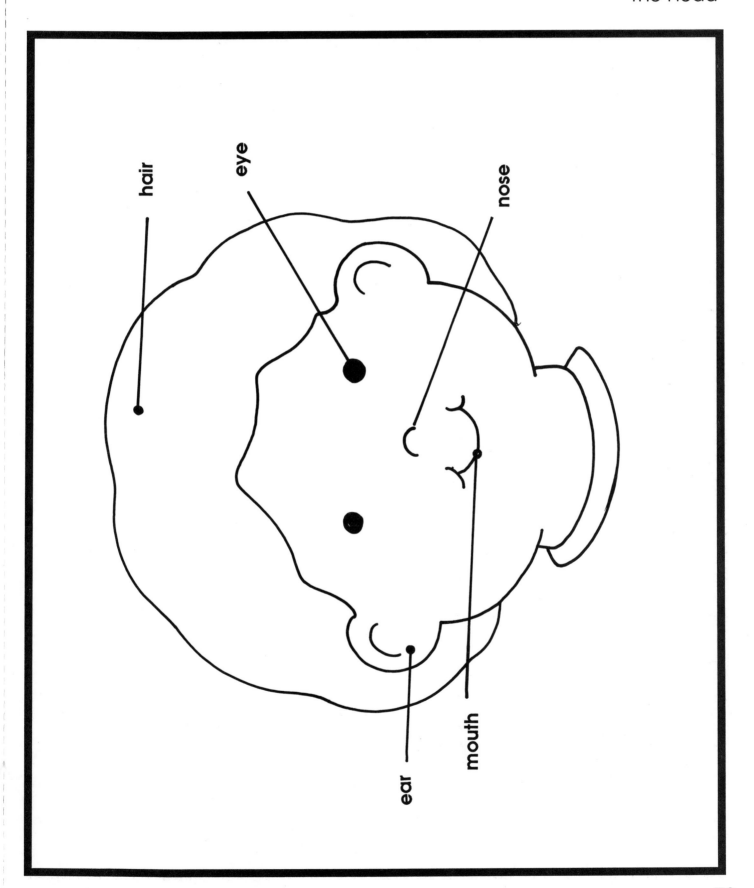

hair

eye

nose

ear

mouth

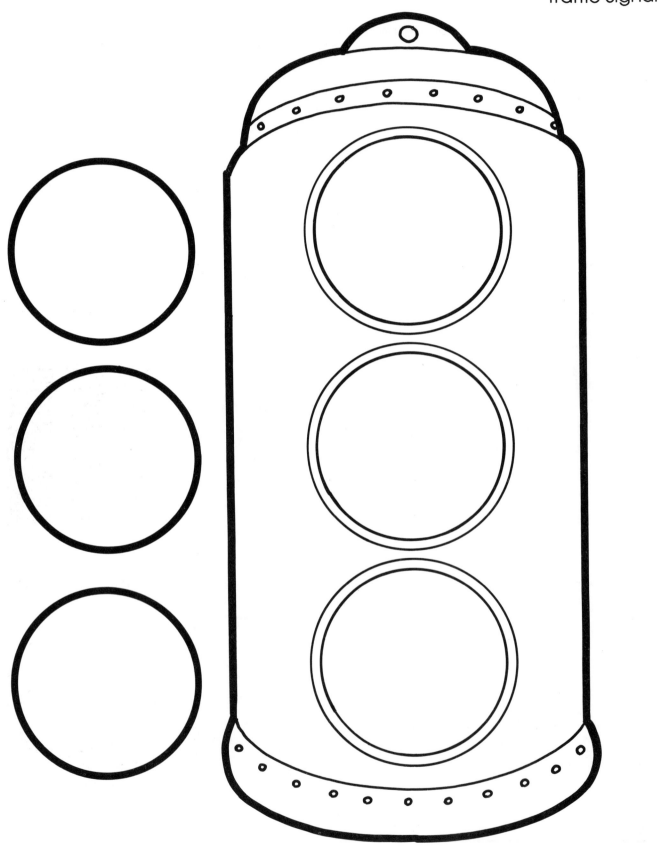

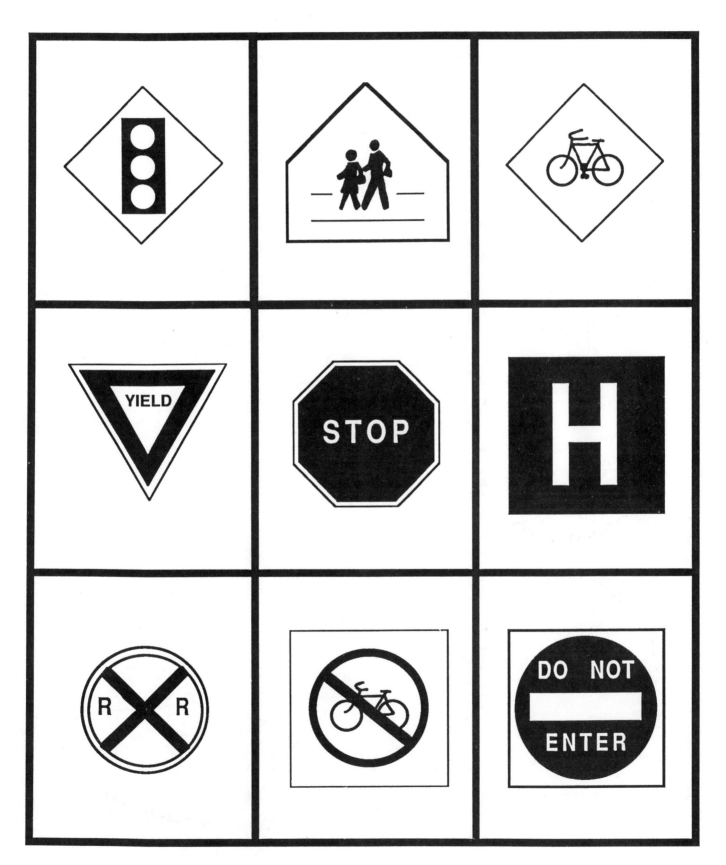

Community Workers

Police Officer, Firefighter, Paramedic

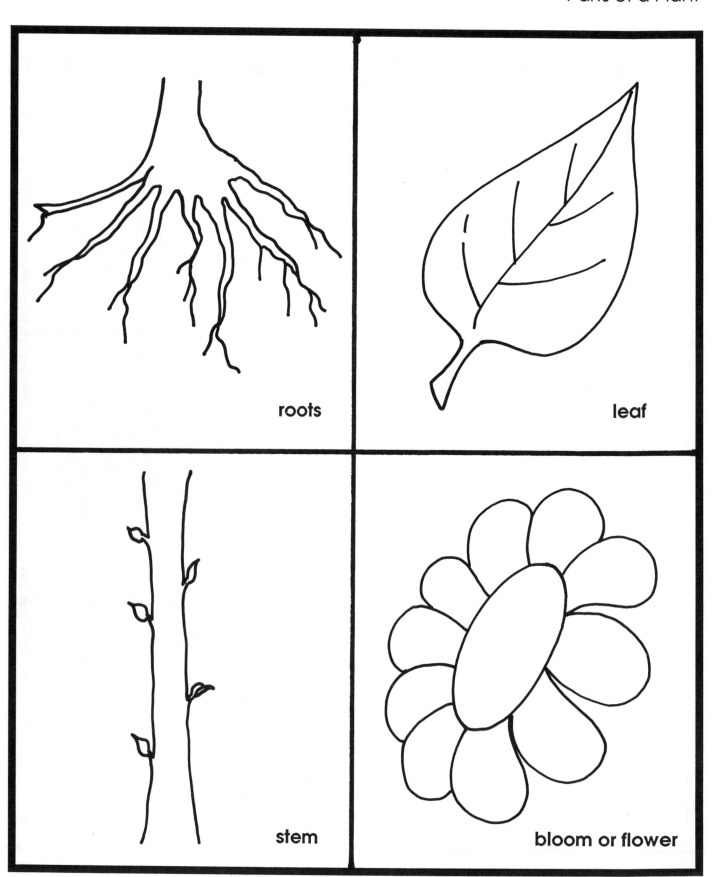

roots

leaf

stem

bloom or flower

Plants

Trees, Leaves, Blooms

Maple Tree

Oak Tree

Pine Tree

Maple Leaf

Oak Leaf

Pine Needles

Maple Seedpod

Acorn

Pine Cone

86

Birds

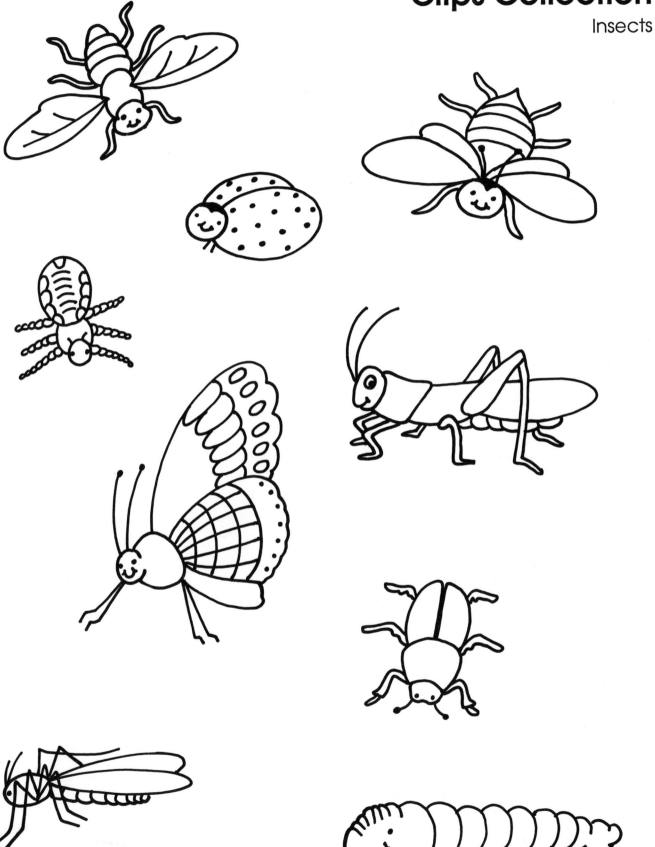

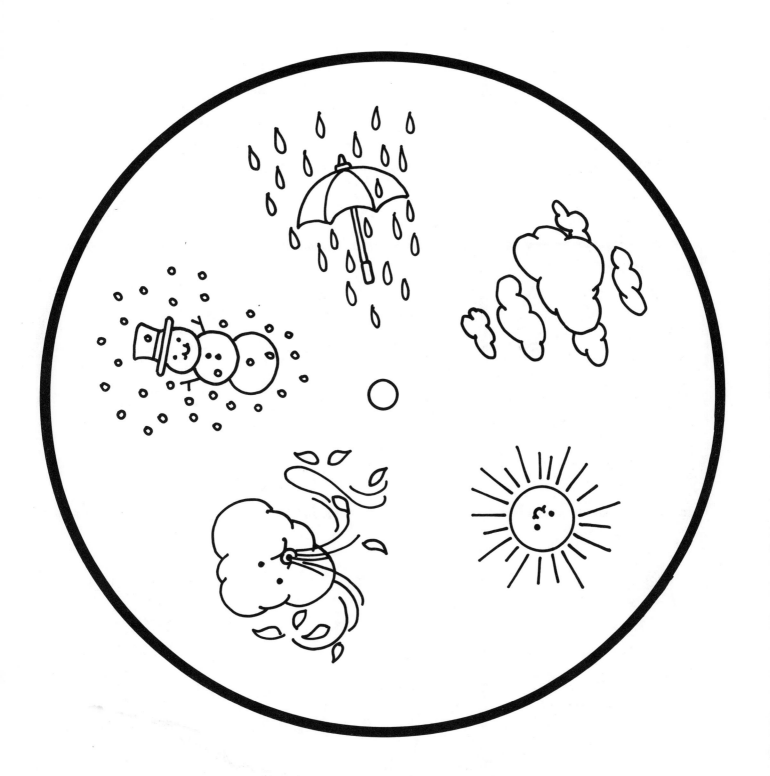

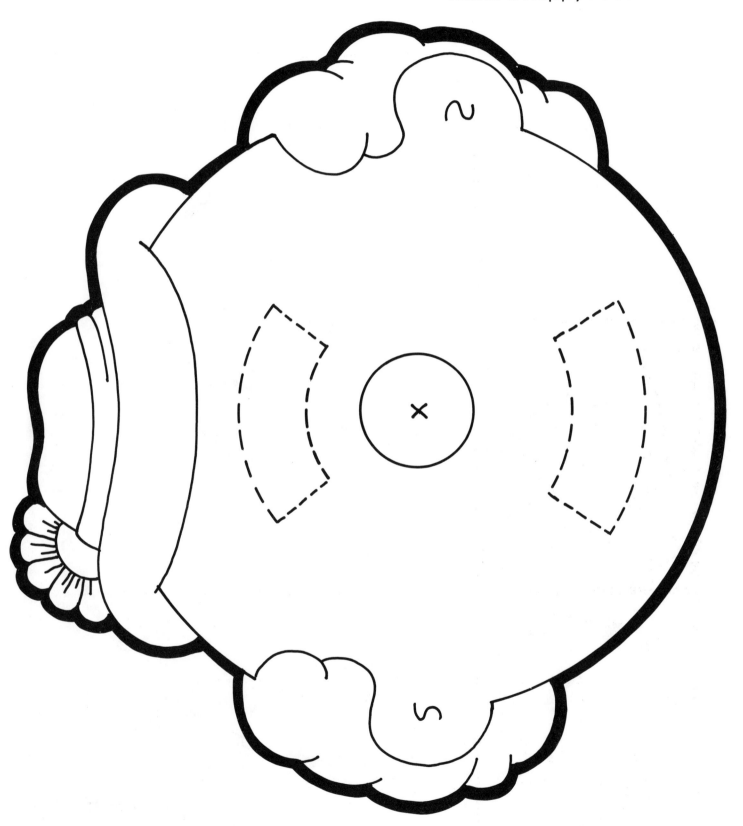

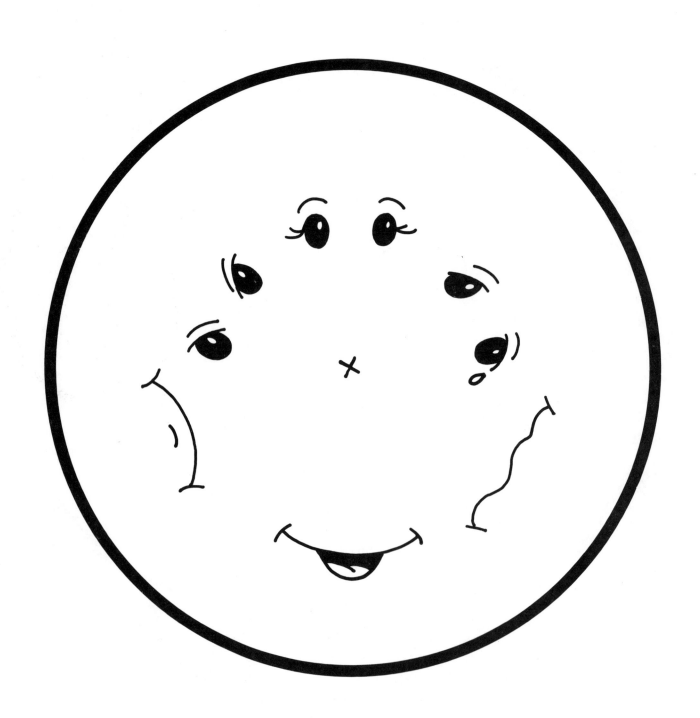

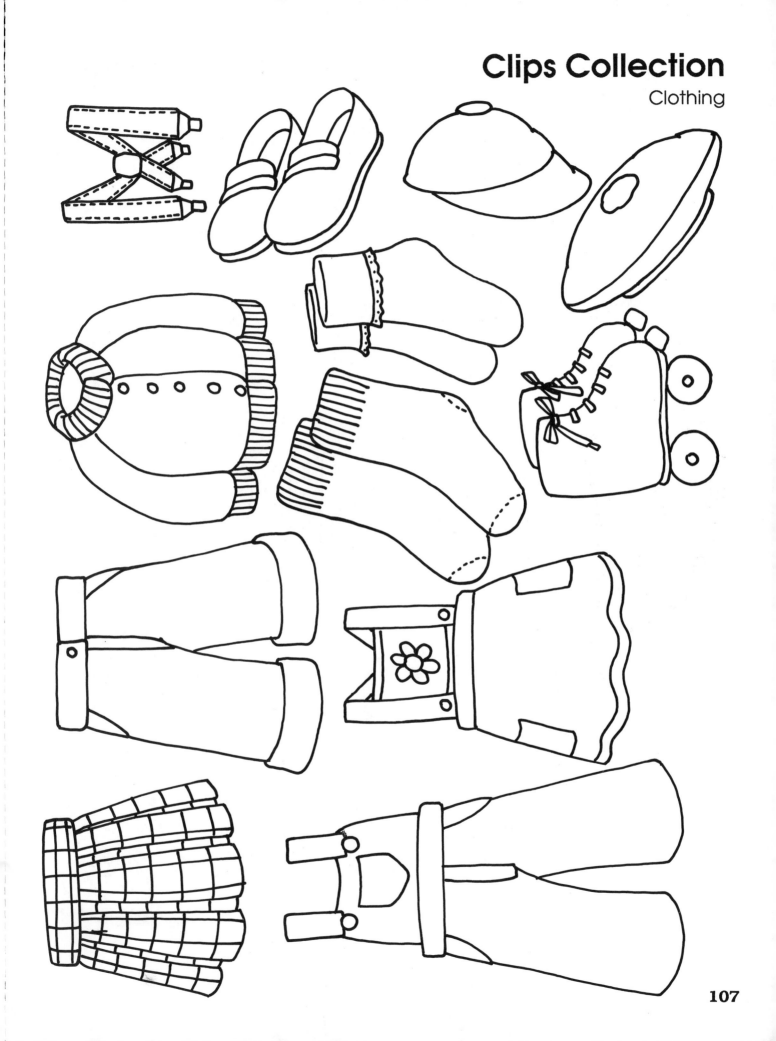

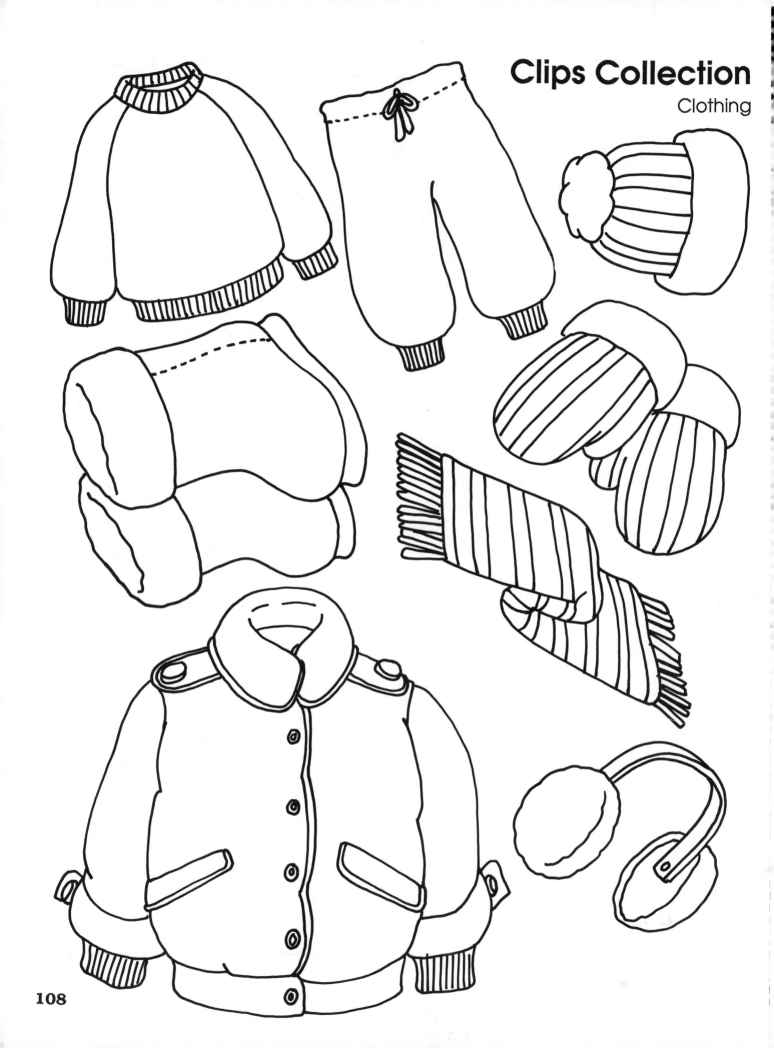

MILK MILK

SOAP

MOUTHWASH

TOOTHPASTE

SHAMPOO

FLOSS

WELCOME TO OPEN HOUSE

RECESS

Quiet, Please!

WELCOME TO OUR SHOW

LET'S READ A BOOK

A Pocketful of Joy!

And 1, and 2....

On the Right Track

Ready, Set, Go!

Happy Birthday!

Creative Writing Paper

Fall

_____

- -

_____

- -

_____

- -

_____

- -

_____

_____

- -

_____

_____

- -

_____

_____

- - - - - - - - - - - - - - - - -

_____

_____

_____

- - - - - - - - - - - - - - - - -

_____

_____

- - - - - - - - - - - - - - - - -

_____

- - - - - - - - - - - - - - - - -

_____

_____

- - - - - - - - - - - - - - - - -

_____

Creative Writing Paper
Spring

Creative Writing Paper

Summer

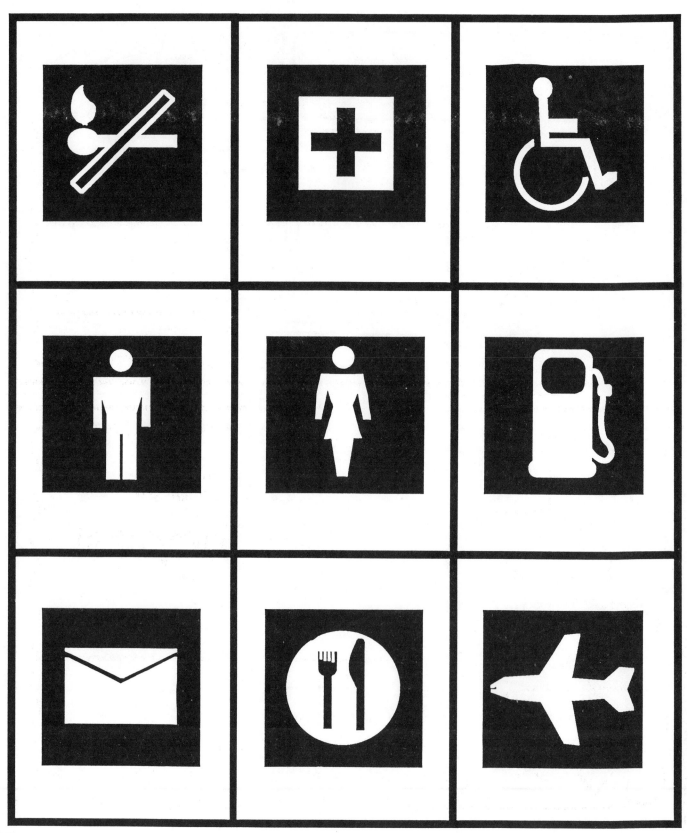

I Know My Colors!

_____
Student

_____
Teacher   Date

I Know My Shapes!

_____
Student

_____
Teacher   Date

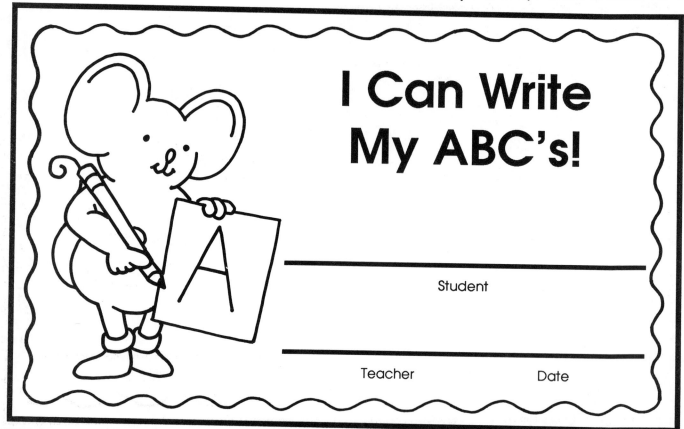

I Can Write My ABC's!

_____

Student

_____

Teacher   Date

I Can Count to 10!

_____

Student

_____

Teacher   Date

I Can Write My Name!

Student

Teacher   Date

I Can Write My Telephone Number!

Student

Teacher   Date

I Know My Right from My Left!

left hand print
here

right hand print
here

_____
Student

_____
Date

I'm a Good Listener!

_____
Student

_____
Teacher

_____
Date

Award Badges

I Can Count to 10

I Can Write My Name!

DUCKY

I Am a Good Listener!

Congratulations on Your Graduation From Kindergarten

Student

Date

Teacher

Happy Birthday to a Very Special Person!

Student

Teacher

Date